Scottish Slimmers
quick

contents

Key to recipes

SERVES two | 000 | 0 | 0

Checks

Calories

Fat grams

All values given in the recipes are for calories, Checks and grams of fat (in that order), excluding No-Check foods, and are **per serving** unless stated otherwise.

jacket jamboree 28

spiced up beans & cheese jacket
sweet chilli prawn jacket
tuna & sweetcorn jacket
minced beef stuffed potato
red pesto chicken & mushroom jacket

something 36
on toast

bruschetta
savoury scrambled eggs
creamy garlic mushrooms
devilled pâté

hot today 42
cold tomorrow

scotch eggs
ham & mushroom quiches
microwave meatloaf
cheese & tomato bread pudding
spaghetti frittata

sandwich
selection

| SERVES one | 275 | 11 | 9 |

chicken
salad wrap

- **1 flour tortilla**
- **25 g/1 oz iceberg lettuce, shredded**
- **60g/2 oz cooked chicken breast**
- **2 cm/1 inch cucumber**
- **1 tomato**
- **1 dspn low-calorie mayonnaise**
- **black pepper**

1 Scatter the shredded lettuce over the flour tortilla.

2 Finely chop the chicken, cucumber and tomato and mix with the mayonnaise. Season with black pepper.

3 Spread the mixture down the centre two-thirds of the tortilla. Fold in the (uncovered) sides of the tortilla and roll up. Cut in half, slightly on the diagonal.

cheese & carrot pitta pockets

SERVES one | 275 11 9

- 60g/2 oz medium pitta bread
- 30g/1 oz half-fat cheddar
- 1 medium carrot
- 1 tomato
- 1 spring onion
- 1 tbsp low-calorie mayonnaise

1 Cut the pitta bread in half and open out to make two pockets.

2 Grate the cheese. Peel and grate the carrot. Finely chop the tomato and spring onion.

3 Mix together the cheese, carrot, tomato, spring onion and mayonnaise and use to fill the 2 pitta pockets.

SERVES one | **310** | **12** | **9**

mexicana cheese sandwich

- 2 medium slices oatbran or half wholemeal/half white bread
- 1 tsp low-fat spread
- 1 dspn sweet chilli sauce
- 30g/1 oz half-fat cheddar or half-fat red leicester cheese, grated
- 1 dspn sweetcorn kernels
- 1 tbsp finely chopped red or green pepper
- 15g/½ oz iceberg lettuce, shredded

1 Spread the bread with the low-fat spread. Spread one slice with the sweet chilli sauce.

2 Sprinkle over the cheese, sweetcorn and chopped pepper.

3 Top with shredded lettuce and the other slice of bread. Press lightly together and cut diagonally in half.

SERVES one | **270** | **11** | **7**

tuna, tomato & olive roll

- 85-100g can tuna in brine, drained
- 1 small tomato, finely chopped
- 4 pimento stuffed olives, sliced
- 1 tbsp low-calorie mayonnaise
- black pepper
- 45g/1½ oz wholemeal roll

1 Mix together the tuna, chopped tomato, olive slices and mayonnaise. Season with black pepper.

2 Cut the roll in half horizontally. If preferred, the roll can be lightly toasted. Top each half roll with half the tuna mixture.

SERVES one | 295 **12** ⑨

brie &
grape sandwich

- 2 medium slices brown bread
- 1 tsp low-fat spread
- 50g/1¾ oz half-fat brie
- 6 seedless green grapes
- black pepper

1 Spread the bread with the low-fat spread.

2 Thinly slice the brie and lay over one slice bread. Halve the grapes and lay over the brie.

3 Season with black pepper. Top with remaining slice of bread, press down lightly and cut into halves or quarters.

SERVES one | 300 **12** ⑩

korma chicken
sandwich

- 1 level dspn low-calorie mayonnaise
- 1 level dspn mango chutney
- ½ level tsp korma curry paste
- 2 medium slices bread
- 15g/½ oz shredded iceberg lettuce
- 30g/1 oz thinly sliced or chopped cooked chicken

1 Mix the mayonnaise, mango chutney and curry paste together in a cup. Use to spread both slices of bread.

2 Cover one slice of bread with the lettuce and chicken. Top with remaining slice of bread, press down lightly and cut into halves or quarters.

cheese, ham & tomato pannini

SERVES one | 305 | 12 | 9

85g/3 oz pannini roll
15g/ ½ oz half-fat cheddar, grated
2 wafer thin slices smoked ham
1 tomato, thinly sliced
black pepper
2 or 3 basil leaves (optional)

1 Pre-heat oven to 190°/gas mark 5.

2 Cut the pannini almost in half horizontally. Fill with the grated cheese, ham and tomato slices. Season with black pepper and add torn basil leaves, if using. Press together lightly.

3 Place in pre-heated oven and cook about 5 minutes, or until crust is warm and crispy and cheese has just melted.

sexy
salads

SERVES one | 200 | 8 | 1

sushi salad

- **115g/4 oz cooked weight boiled rice or 45g/ 1½ oz dry weight**
- **chopped cucumber**
- **1-2 sliced spring onions**
- **3 seafood sticks, chopped**
- **light soy sauce**
- **salad leaves**
- **sushi ginger (optional)**

1 If you don't have any leftover cooked rice, boil the dry rice according to pack instructions. Rinse the rice in cold water and drain thoroughly.

2 Mix together the rice, cucumber, spring onions and seafood sticks.

3 Season with soy sauce to taste and serve on a bed of salad leaves. A few slivers of pickled sushi ginger makes a delicious tangy accompaniment.

green pasta salad

SERVES one 250 10 7

- **45g/1½ oz green (spinach) pasta**
- **1 small courgette, sliced**
- **1 small stick of celery, sliced**
- **4 cherry tomatoes, halved**
- **1 tbsp oil-free vinaigrette dressing**
- **30g/1 oz feta cheese**
- **a few basil leaves, torn**

1 Cook the pasta in lightly salted boiling water until just tender. Rinse in cold water and drain well.

2 Sprinkle sliced courgettes with salt, leave in a colander to "draw" for about 30 minutes. Rinse well, pat dry on kitchen paper and add to pasta.

3 Add celery and tomatoes and stir in dressing.

4 Top with crumbled feta and garnish with torn basil leaves.

SERVES
one	**250** **10** **4**

sesame
chicken wrappers

- **4 medium size crisp lettuce leaves (e.g. iceberg or romaine)**
- **a few strips of cucumber**
- **¼ red pepper, cut into strips**
- **1-2 spring onions, cut into strips**
- **1 medium skinless chicken breast**
- **1 tsp runny honey**
- **1 tsp light soy sauce**
- **spray oil**
- **1 tsp sesame seeds**
- **4 tsp hoisin sauce**

1 Arrange lettuce leaves on a plate and put one or two strips of cucumber, red pepper and spring onion on each.

2 Cut chicken breast into small strips. Mix honey and soy sauce together and coat the chicken strips with the mixture. Spray a small pan with oil and heat. Stir-fry chicken and mixture over medium heat about 5 minutes or until browned and cooked through. (If heat is too high, honey will burn.)

3 Add the sesame seeds and stir-fry a further 1-2 minutes.

4 Divide the chicken between the lettuce leaves and top each with a teaspoon of hoisin sauce. Wrap the lettuce around the chicken to eat.

SERVES **four** | **60** **2.5** ①

banana salad

- **2 medium bananas**
- **1 dspn lemon juice**
- **1 green pepper, chopped**
- **2 tomatoes, chopped**
- **5 cm/2 inches cucumber, chopped**
- **1 tbsp dessicated coconut**
- **1 tsp garam masala or curry powder, or to taste**

1 Peel and slice the bananas. Place in a bowl and toss in the lemon juice to prevent browning.

2 Add remaining ingredients and mix together well.

3 Particularly good served as a side dish with curries. Or for lunch, serve in a 60 g/2 oz pitta bread (add 150 calories 6 Checks 2g fat).

warm bacon & egg salad

SERVES **two** | 290 **12** ⑩

- baby spinach leaves or mixed salad leaves
- oil-free dressing
- 3 back bacon medallions
- 50g/1¾ oz slice ciabatta or crusty bread
- 1 clove garlic
- spray oil
- 1 medium egg
- dash of vinegar

1 Arrange some baby spinach or mixed salad leaves on a plate and sprinkle with the oil-free dressing.

2 Grill the bacon medallions, chop and sprinkle over the leaves.

3 Cut the garlic clove in half and use the cut surface to rub all over the bread. Spray with oil and toast lightly.

4 Fill a non-stick pan with 2 cm/1 inch cold water and dash of vinegar. Bring to a gentle simmer, crack in egg and poach 3-4 minutes. Place the egg on the toasted bread and serve with the salad and bacon.

note...

Many supermarkets now sell back bacon medallions, but if you can't get them, use just the round, lean part from 3 rashers of back bacon.

hot stuff

SERVES **two** |285 **12** 6

steak & new potato brochettes

4 bamboo skewers
225g/8 oz trimmed, lean rump steak
2 tbsp red wine
1 clove garlic, chopped
½ tsp herbes de provence
black pepper
2 small red onions, each cut into 6 wedges
1 medium courgette, cut into 12-16 slices
12 small new potatoes, boiled in skin
salt
spray oil

1 Soak the bamboo skewers in water at least 30 minutes to prevent scorching.

2 Cut the steak into 12 cubes. Mix together the wine, garlic, herbs and black pepper in a shallow dish. Marinate steak cubes in the mixture at least 30 minutes.

3 Lightly steam, or microwave on high about 1 minute, onion wedges and courgette slices until just tender.

4 Remove steak from marinade. Season steak and vegetables lightly with salt. Thread steak onto skewers alternating with cooked new potatoes, onion wedges and courgettes. Spray lightly with oil.

5 Cook under a pre-heated grill, turning occasionally, until steak is done to your liking. Alternatively cook on the barbecue.

brunch omelette

SERVES **one** 255 **10** ⑮

- 1 very low-fat sausage (e.g. Wall's Lean Recipe)
- 1 turkey rasher
- 2 mushrooms
- 1 tomato, thickly sliced
- 2 medium eggs, beaten
- spray oil
- black pepper

1 Pre-heat the grill and cook the sausage about 5 minutes or until browned on one side. Turn over the sausage and add the mushrooms and tomato slices to the grill and cook 5 minutes.

2 Turn over the mushrooms and tomatoes and add the turkey rasher. Cook a further 2 minutes, then turn over the rasher and cook 1 minute more.

3 Slice the sausage, mushrooms and turkey rasher.

4 Spray a non-stick pan with oil and heat. Spread the sliced sausage, mushrooms, turkey rasher and tomatoes over the base of the pan. Pour over the beaten egg and season with black pepper.

5 Cook gently until underneath is set then pop the pan under the grill until top is just set. Slide the omelette onto a serving plate.

| SERVES four | 270 | 11 | 15 |

grilled halloumi snack

- **salad leaves**
- **16 cherry tomatoes, halved**
- **lemon juice**
- **black pepper**
- **4 medium slices wholemeal bread**
- **240-250g pack halloumi cheese**

1 Pre-heat grill to moderate.

2 Arrange salad leaves and cherry tomatoes on 4 plates. Sprinkle with lemon juice and black pepper.

3 Toast the bread. Cut into small cubes and scatter over salad.

4 Cut the halloumi into 8 slices. Place on grill and cook until golden. Turn over and brown other side.

5 Arrange 2 slices of grilled halloumi on each salad and serve warm.

SERVES **one** 310 **12** ⑤

macaroni, peas & bacon

- **60g/2 oz quick cook macaroni**
- **1 small onion, chopped**
- **1 rasher well trimmed back bacon, chopped**
- **2 tbsp frozen peas**
- **3 tbsp canned chopped tomatoes**
- **½ tsp basil or chilli powder**
- **salt and pepper**

1 Cook macaroni in lightly salted boiling water until just tender. Drain well.

2 Put onion in a microwavable dish with 1 tbsp water and microwave on high 1 minute.

3 Add bacon and microwave 2 minutes.

4 Add peas, tomatoes and chilli or basil and microwave 2 minutes more.

5 Stir well and toss together with the drained macaroni. Season to taste and serve immediately.

stir-fried pasta

SERVES one 280 **11** ⑥

- 45g/1½ oz pasta shapes
- 2 turkey rashers
- 1 small onion, chopped
- 1 small red or green pepper, chopped
- 1 small courgette, chopped
- 4 mushrooms, chopped
- spray oil
- pinch of mixed herbs
- salt and pepper
- 30g/1 oz half-fat cheddar

1 Cook the pasta in lightly salted boiling water until just tender. Drain well.

2 Grill or dry-fry the turkey rashers, then chop.

3 Spray pan with oil and stir-fry the onion, peppers, courgettes and mushrooms until crisp-tender. Add 1-2 tbsp water, if necessary, to prevent sticking.

4 Add turkey rashers and pasta to the pan and heat through. Serve topped with grated cheese.

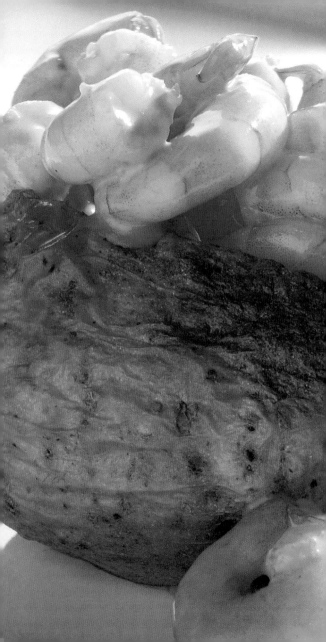

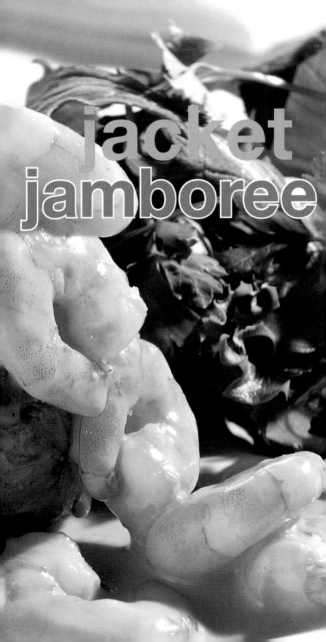

jacket
jamboree

SERVES one | 300 **12** ③

spiced-up beans & cheese jacket

- **200g/7 oz baking potato**
- **200g/7 oz reduced-sugar-and-salt baked beans**
- **a few drops worcester sauce or tabasco sauce**
- **15g/½ oz half-fat cheddar or half-fat red leicester, grated**
- **no-Check salad to serve**

1 Scrub potato and prick with a fork or pointed knife. Either bake in a pre-heated oven 200°C/gas mark 6 approximately 75 minutes, or microwave on high about 6-7 minutes and, if you have time, pop into a hot oven 10-15 minutes to crisp up skin.

2 Put the beans and Worcester sauce or Tabasco sauce into a small pan and heat gently, stirring.

3 Cut a deep cross in the potato and gently squeeze to open out. Top with the beans and grated cheese and serve with no-Check salad.

sweet chilli prawn jacket

SERVES one 305 12 ①

- **225g/8 oz baking potato**
- **2 spring onions, sliced**
- **85g/3 oz frozen sliced mixed peppers**
- **85g/3 oz cooked prawns, defrosted if frozen**
- **1 tbsp sweet chilli sauce**
- **no-Check salad to serve**

1 Scrub potato and prick with a fork or pointed knife. Either bake in a pre-heated oven 200°C/gas mark 6 approximately 75 minutes, or microwave on high about 7 minutes and, if you have time, pop into a hot oven 10-15 minutes to crisp up skin.

2 Cook onions and peppers in a small non-stick saucepan until softened and starting to brown.

3 Add prawns and cook gently 1-2 minutes to heat through. Stir in sweet chilli sauce.

4 Cut a deep cross in the potato and gently squeeze to open out. Top with the sweet chilli prawns mixture and serve with no-Check salad.

SERVES one | 300 12 3 | tuna & sweetcorn jacket

- **200g/7 oz baking potato**
- **85-100g can tuna in brine, drained**
- **2 dspn sweetcorn kernels**
- **1 tbsp low-calorie mayonnaise**
- **black pepper**
- **no-Check salad to serve**

1 Scrub potato and prick with a fork or pointed knife. Either bake in a pre-heated oven 200°C/gas mark 6 approximately 75 minutes, or microwave on high about 6-7 minutes and, if you have time, pop into a hot oven 10-15 minutes to crisp up skin.

2 Flake the tuna and mix with the sweetcorn and mayonnaise. Season to taste with black pepper.

3 Cut a deep slit in the potato and gently open out. Fill with the tuna and sweetcorn mixture and serve with no-Check salad.

SERVES
one **300** **12** **7**

minced beef
stuffed potato

- **200g/7 oz baking potato**
- **75g/2½ oz lean beef mince**
- **1 tbsp finely chopped onion**
- **1 small carrot, finely grated**
- **1 dspn gravy powder**
- **1 tbsp water**
- **1 tsp tomato purée**
- **1 tsp chopped parsley**
- **little skimmed milk**
- **salt and pepper**
- **no-Check vegetables or salad to serve**

1 Scrub potato and prick with a fork or pointed knife. Either bake in a pre-heated oven 200°C/gas mark 6 approximately 75 minutes, or microwave on high about 6-7 minutes and, if you have time, pop into a hot oven 10-15 minutes to crisp up skin.

2 Cook the mince, onion and carrot together in a small non-stick pan.

3 Mix the gravy powder with the water and tomato purée and stir into the cooked mince together with the parsley.

4 Cut cooked potato in half and scoop out centres, reserving skins. Mash scooped-out potato with a little skimmed milk. Mix potato with mince and season to taste.

5 Spoon mince mixture back into reserved potato skins, fork up and brown under a pre-heated grill. Serve with no-Check vegetables or salad.

red pesto chicken & mushroom jacket

SERVES two 300 12 9

- 2 x 200g/7 oz baking potatoes
- 1 medium skinless chicken breast
- 115g/4 oz mushrooms
- spray oil
- 2 level tbsp red pesto
- no-Check vegetables or salad to serve

1 Scrub potatoes and prick with a fork or pointed knife. Either bake in a pre-heated oven 200°C/gas mark 6 approximately 75 minutes, or microwave on high about 10-12 minutes and, if you have time, pop into a hot oven 10-15 minutes to crisp up skin.

2 Use kitchen scissors to snip the chicken into small cubes. Chop the mushrooms.

3 Spray a pan with oil and heat. Sauté the chicken and mushrooms approximately 5 minutes or until the chicken is cooked through. Stir in the pesto sauce.

4 Cut the potatoes in half and lay two halves on each serving plate. Divide the pesto chicken and mushroom mixture between the two servings, piling it on the cut surfaces of the potato and serve with no-Check vegetables or salad.

something **on** toast

SERVES one | 270 **11** **6** # bruschetta with smoked salmon topping

- 4 x 15g/½ oz slices ciabatta bread
- 1 clove garlic, cut in half
- 60g/2 oz smoked salmon trimmings, chopped
- 2 spring onions, finely chopped
- 60g/2 oz fat-free natural fromage frais
- squeeze of lemon juice
- black pepper
- snipped chives to garnish

1 Lightly toast the ciabatta. Rub the cut sides of the ciabatta with the garlic clove.

2 Mix together the smoked salmon, spring onions and fromage frais. Season with a squeeze of lemon juice and black pepper.

3 Pile the smoked salmon topping onto the ciabatta and garnish with snipped chives.

SERVES one | 260 **10** **4** # bruschetta with butterbean topping

1 Prepare ciabatta as above.

2 Mix together ½ small finely chopped red onion, 2 finely chopped tomatoes, 200g can drained butterbeans and season to taste. Pile onto ciabatta and garnish with torn basil leaves.

savoury scrambled eggs on toast

SERVES **one** 270 **11** **14**

- **2 medium eggs**
- **2-3 mushrooms, chopped**
- **1 tomato, finely chopped**
- **2 spring onions, chopped**
- **1 tsp low-fat spread**
- **1 dspn skimmed milk**
- **salt and pepper**
- **1 medium slice wholemeal bread**

1 Beat eggs in a microwavable jug. Add remaining ingredients and beat lightly.

2 Toast the bread.

3 Place jug in the microwave and cook 1 minute 15 seconds on high. Beat again.

4 Cook a further minute and stir. If necessary, cook in further bursts of 10 seconds, stirring in between but do not overcook as this will impair taste and texture.

5 Serve savoury scrambled eggs on the toast.

SERVES
one

105 4 1 garlic mushrooms & toast

- spray oil
- **85g/3oz mushrooms, chopped**
- **1 small clove garlic, crushed**
- **1 medium slice wholemeal bread**
- **1 rounded tbsp fat-free natural fromage frais**
- **1 tsp finely chopped parsley**
- **black pepper**

1 Spray a small saucepan with oil and heat. Add the mushrooms and garlic and cook gently for a few minutes, stirring now and again, until juices start to run.

2 Toast the bread and cut into 2 or 4 triangles.

3 Take the saucepan off the heat and stir in the fromage frais, parsley and black pepper.

4 Put the garlic mushrooms on a serving plate with toast triangles beside, so that the toast will not go soft.

devilled kipper pâté

- **2 x 190g cans John West Kipper Fillets in oil, drained**
- **30g/1oz low-fat spread, melted**
- **2 tsp mustard**
- **½ tsp ground cloves**
- **1 small onion, peeled and grated**
- **1-2 tbsp white or white wine vinegar**
- **4 medium slices wholemeal bread**

1 Place the kippers in a bowl and mash.

2 Slowly add the melted spread, then beat in the mustard and cloves.

3 Stir in the onion, then sufficient vinegar to give a spreadable consistency. Turn into 4 small ramekins and chill for 1 hour.

4 Toast the bread and cut into triangles just before serving with the pâté

hot
today

cold
tomorrow

SERVES **four** | **200** **8** **12**

scotch eggs

- **4 large low-fat sausages**
- **1 tsp mixed herbs**
- **4 medium eggs, hard-boiled and cooled**
- **a little skimmed milk**
- **1 medium slice wholemeal bread, made into crumbs**

1 Pre-heat oven to 180°C/gas mark 4.

2 Remove skins from sausages and mash in a bowl. Mix in the herbs.

3 Peel the hard-boiled eggs. Divide the sausage meat into 4 and wrap one portion around each egg.

4 Dip each sausage-wrapped egg into the milk and then into the breadcrumbs.

5 Place eggs on a rack over a baking tray and bake approximately 30-40 minutes until the crumbs are crisp, turning once or twice during cooking.

6 Either serve warm, or allow to cool and store in the fridge to eat cold.

ham & mushroom quiches

SERVES four 225 9 8

- **115g/4 oz self-raising flour**
- **salt and pepper**
- **60g /2 oz low-fat spread**
- **2 tbsp cold water**
- **1 medium egg**
- **200g/7 oz quark skimmed milk soft cheese**
- **45g/1½ oz or 4 wafer slices ham, chopped**
- **2-3 mushrooms, thinly sliced**
- **no-Check salad to serve**

1 Mix flour with small pinch of salt and rub in low-fat spread until it resembles breadcrumbs. Mix with water to make a dough. Wrap in clingfilm and allow pastry to rest 30 minutes.

2 Pre-heat oven to 200°C/gas mark 6.

3 Roll out pastry to line 4 individual flan or Yorkshire pudding tins approximately 10 cm/4 inches diameter. Bake blind 5 minutes.

4 Beat egg with quark and add ham, mushrooms and seasoning to taste. Fill pastry cases with mixture and return to oven approximately 25 minutes or until set and golden.

5 Either eat warm, or allow to cool on a rack to crisp pastry and eat cold. Store covered in the fridge to eat the following day.

SERVES
four | 175 **7** **8**

microwave
meatloaf

- **75g/2½ oz small onion, chopped**
- **75g/2½ oz carrot, coarsely grated**
- **400g/14 oz lean minced beef or minced steak**
- **1 dspn worcester sauce**
- **1 dspn tomato purée**
- **1 dspn dried parsley**
- **2 Bovril cubes**
- **1 medium egg, beaten**

1 In a 1 litre/2 pint microwavable casserole or loaf pan, microwave the onions and carrots, covered, on high 4 minutes, or until soft.

2 Mix in mince, Worcester sauce, tomato purée and parsley. Crumble in Bovril cubes, add beaten egg and mix thoroughly.

3 Microwave on medium (approximately 500 watts) 12 minutes. Stand 5 minutes then drain off surplus fat.

4 Either serve warm with no-Check vegetables, or to eat cold, allow to cool, cover and store in the fridge. Serve sliced with no-Check salad.

cheese & tomato bread pudding

SERVES one | 350 14 12

- **2 medium slices bread**
- **2 tsp tomato purée**
- **spray oil**
- **1 large tomato, sliced**
- **pinch of mixed herbs**
- **30g/1 oz half-fat cheddar**
- **½ tsp grated parmesan cheese**
- **1 medium egg**
- **100 ml/3½ fl.oz skimmed milk**
- **½ tsp dijon mustard**
- **½ tsp vegetable bouillon or ½ crumbled vegetable Oxo cube**

1 Spread bread with tomato purée and cut each slice into 4 triangles.

2 Spray ovenproof gratin dish with oil. Lay 4 triangles of bread in the bottom. Top with half the tomato slices, some herbs, half the parmesan and a few "shavings" of cheddar (saving most for the top). Layer remaining bread, tomatoes, herbs and parmesan.

3 Lightly beat egg and make up to 150 ml/5 fl.oz with the milk. Stir in the mustard and bouillon or Oxo. Pour mixture over bread and tomatoes and leave 20 minutes to absorb. Grate remaining cheese and sprinkle over top.

4 Pre-heat oven to 190°C/gas mark 5.

5 Bake approximately 20 minutes or until set and lightly browned. Serve either warm with no-Check salad or vegetables, or allow to cool and store covered in the fridge to eat cold.

| SERVES two | 300 | 12 7 |

spaghetti frittata

- 100g/3½ oz spaghetti
- 1 medium courgette, chopped
- 85g/3 oz mushrooms, chopped
- 1 large egg, beaten
- 2 dspn grated parmesan cheese
- 200g/7 oz low-fat pasta sauce with mushrooms or vegetables
- spray oil

1 Cook spaghetti in lightly salted boiling water until tender, adding courgettes and mushrooms about 4 minutes before end of cooking.

2 Drain spaghetti and vegetables, rinse under cold water and drain thoroughly. Return to pan and stir in beaten egg, parmesan cheese and pasta sauce.

3 Spray a good quality non-stick pan with oil and heat. Tip the pasta into the pan and press down to cover base of pan. Cook over moderate heat about 5-7 minutes to brown underneath.

4 Place a plate over the pan and invert the frittata onto the plate. Re-spray pan with oil and heat. Slide frittata back into the pan and cook for a further 5-7 minutes to brown other side.

5 Slide frittata on to a plate, cut in half and eat warm. Or, allow frittata to cool, cover and store in fridge and serve cold cut into slices or wedges with no-Check salad.

note...

Low-fat pasta sauce can be any having less than 3g fat per 100g and up to about 50 calories per 100g.